Dora's Colors and Shapes Adventure

written by Phoebe Beinstein & Christine Ricci
illustrated by Susan Hall

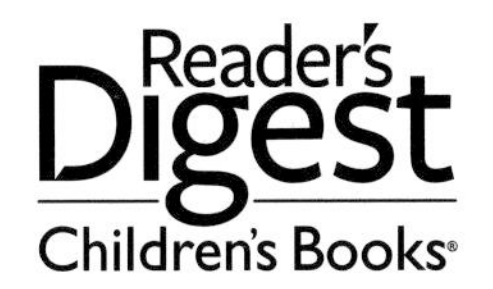

New York, New York • Montréal, Québec • Bath, United Kingdom

¡Hola! I'm Dora. Today we're going on a colors and shapes adventure. I'm going to visit my friends and along the way, I'm going to see how many colors and shapes I can find. I can't wait to see what other surprises we might find.

The house I live in is yellow. *¡Amarillo!* Do you see other yellow things here?

Exploring la Casa

Find felt pieces of Dora and her friends and put them on the play scene. Find pretty yellow flowers and plants to decorate the felt play scene.

Exploring Boots's Treehouse

Boots likes climbing up the rope ladder to his treehouse. Find felt pieces of Boots and other things you might find around a treehouse and put them in the scene.

There's my friend Boots. He lives in a brown tree house. *¡Marrón!* There are lots of brown things near Boots's tree house. What other brown things do you see here?

Exploring Benny's Barn

Find felt pieces of Benny and other red things to put in the scene.

Boots and I are going to visit Benny. *¡Mira!* Benny is waving to us.

Benny lives in a red barn. *¡Rojo!* There are lots of red things in his yard, too. Do you see anything else that's red here?

Let's go see Tico in the Nutty Forest. Tico lives in a tree filled with acorns. The leaves on his tree are green. *¡Verde!* What else is green in the Nutty Forest?

Go Nutty in Nutty Forest

Lots of plants and animals live in the Nutty Forest. Find felt pieces of Tico and things you might find in a forest and put them in the scene.

Fill the Garden!

Isa loves planting flowers in her garden. Find felt pieces of Isa and pink things and put them in the scene.

Look, Boots. There's Isa in her Flowery Garden. Isa's garden is full of pretty pink flowers. *¡Flores rosadas!* Do you see anything else that's pink?

Fiesta Time!

The Fiesta Trio makes music, and you need to make a party to go with it. Find felt pieces of the Fiesta Trio, Dora and her friends, and put them in the scene.

We made it through the Flowery Garden, and the Fiesta Trio are playing us a tune to celebrate! Let's dance as they play us a song in their orange shell! *¡Anaranjado!* What else is orange?

Let's go to the rainforest and visit *nuestro amigo*, Señor Tucán.

Señor Tucán's nest is high up in a tree and is made of purple leaves. *¡Morado!* What else do you see that is purple?

What's Up?

Señor Tucán flies through the sky, high above the trees. Find felt pieces of things you might find in the sky or a rainforest and put them in the scene.

Now we're going to pick blueberries on Blueberry Hill. *¡Cuidado!* There's the foxhole where Swiper the fox lives. He'll try to swipe our blueberries unless we say ... "Swiper, no swiping!"

Blueberries are blue! *¡Azul!* What else can you see that is blue on Blueberry Hill?

Blueberry Adventures

Dora enjoys picking berries on Blueberry Hill. Find felt pieces of Dora, Boots, Swiper, and anything blue and put them in the scene.

¡Mira! There's a rainbow! Look at all the colors! Will you name the colors in the rainbow? What colors do you see around you?

Explore the Rainbow!

Rainbows usually have six colors: red, orange, yellow, green, blue, and purple. Find a felt piece with a rainbow and add it to the scene. Find other pieces with those colors and put them in the scene, too.

There's a big surprise at the end of the rainbow. Let's go find it! *¡Vámonos!* Who do we need to ask when we don't know which way to go? Map!

Map says we need to go across Crocodile Lake and over the Icky Sticky Sand. And that's how we'll get to the end of the rainbow.

Map Making

Map always knows the best way to get somewhere. Find felt pieces of Dora, Boots, a rainbow, and Map, and put them in the scene.

So first, we have to go to Crocodile Lake. Do you see Crocodile Lake?

There it is! But it's so far. How will we get there quickly? *¡Sí!* Tico's car! The tires on Tico's car are circles! *¡Círculos!* Do you see two blue circles and two yellow circles?

Hop in!

Tico drives a yellow car. Find felt pieces of Dora and Boots, and Tico driving his car, and put them in the scene.

We made it to Crocodile Lake! Let's thank Tico for the ride. *¡Gracias, Tico!*

Oh! *¡Sí!* We can take that sailboat with the triangle-shaped sail! *¡Los triángulos!* How many triangles do you see on Crocodile Lake?

Sailing Time!

Find felt pieces of the sailboats, Dora, Boots, and Tico and put them in the scene.

Cross the Sand!

Find felt pieces of Dora, Boots, a bridge, and a brown rectangular sign and put them in the scene.

We made it across Crocodile Lake! And look! There's a sign. It says, "*¡Cuidado!* Icky Sticky Sand Ahead!" We have to cross the sand to get to the rainbow. What can we use to cross it? *¡El puente!* The bridge!

The bridge has rectangle-shaped pieces of wood in it. Do you see any rectangles in the picture?

¡Cuidado!
Icky Sticky
Sand Ahead

Up, Up and Away

Benny loves soaring through the sky in his balloon. Find felt pieces of Benny, his balloon, a rainbow, and things that fly and put them in the scene.

We made it to the rainbow! There it is! But what can we use to get to the top of the rainbow?

Ah! Benny can help with his hot-air balloon. His balloon looks like a big circle. Do you see a circle in this picture?

Rainbow's End

Everyone loves flying in Benny's hot-air balloon. Find felt pieces of the balloon, the rainbow, a treasure, and Dora and all her friends and put them in the scene.

¡Lo hicimos! We did it! We made it to the end of the rainbow. And there's the surprise at the end of the rainbow—toys! *¡Los juguetes!* Do you see a blue oval in this picture?

Say the Colors Two Ways

Yellow
amarillo

Brown
marrón

Red
rojo

Green
verde

Pink
rosado

Orange
anaranjado

Purple
morado

Blue
azul

Say the Shapes Two Ways

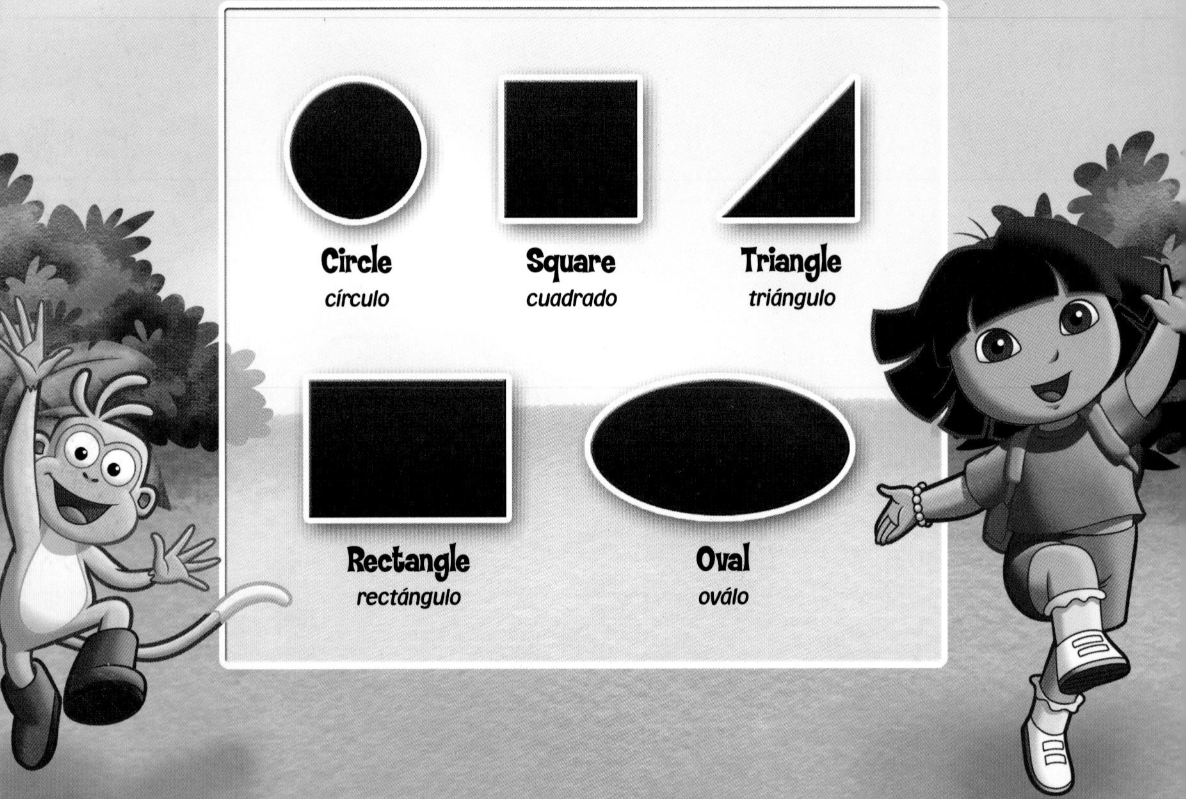

Circle
círculo

Square
cuadrado

Triangle
triángulo

Rectangle
rectángulo

Oval
oválo